Play-Doh

100 THINGS TO SPOT

THIS BOOK BELONGS TO

....

centum

LITTLE BEE IS HIDING IN THE SEEK AND FIND SCENES – CAN YOU FIND HIM?

I'll be hiding!

PLAY-DOH 100 THINGS TO SPOT
A CENTUM BOOK 978-1-910917-94-7
© 2017 Hasbro. All Rights Reserved.
Published in Great Britain by Centum Books Ltd
Centum Books, 20 Devon Square, Newton Abbot,
Devon, TQ12 2HR, UK
books@centumbooksltd.co.uk
CENTUM BOOKS Limited Reg. No. 07641486
This edition published 2017
A CIP catalogue record for this book is available
from the British Library.
Printed in China
1 3 5 7 9 10 8 6 4 2

You're going to love exploring the Play-Doh scenes as you count and spot on the farm, under the sea, in the jungle, in the garden and around the town.

Plus there are lots more puzzles to test your spotting skills, as well as mini challenges in the seek and find scenes.

ARE YOU READY?
THEN LET'S GET SPOTTING!

THE ANSWERS CAN BE FOUND AT THE BACK OF THE BOOK.

There are number lines to help you with counting.
Try counting from one to ten using the line below.

1 2 3 4 5 6 7 8 9 10

Seek and Find

On the Farm

Welcome to Play-Doh farm. It's always so bright and busy here. Can you find the five friendly farm animals?

Can you find five pieces of corn in this picture?

Cluck! Cluck!

Oink! Who lives here?

Who is wearing a hat?

Can you make a friend for this little duck?

Baa! Baa!

Quack! Quack!

How many cockerals can you count?

Neigh!

What colour is the turkey?

Can you find the other half of the apple for the horse to eat?

4

1 2 3 4 5 6 7 8 9 10

Can you find?

Woof!

What is a baby dog called?

What shape are the tractor's wheels?

Meow!

Moo!

hen

chick

cow

horse

lamb

5

Ducks in a Row

Find the duck with the blue beak.

Find the duck with orange feathers.

Find the duck swimming a different way to its friends.

If you made a Play-Doh pond for these ducks, what colour would it be?

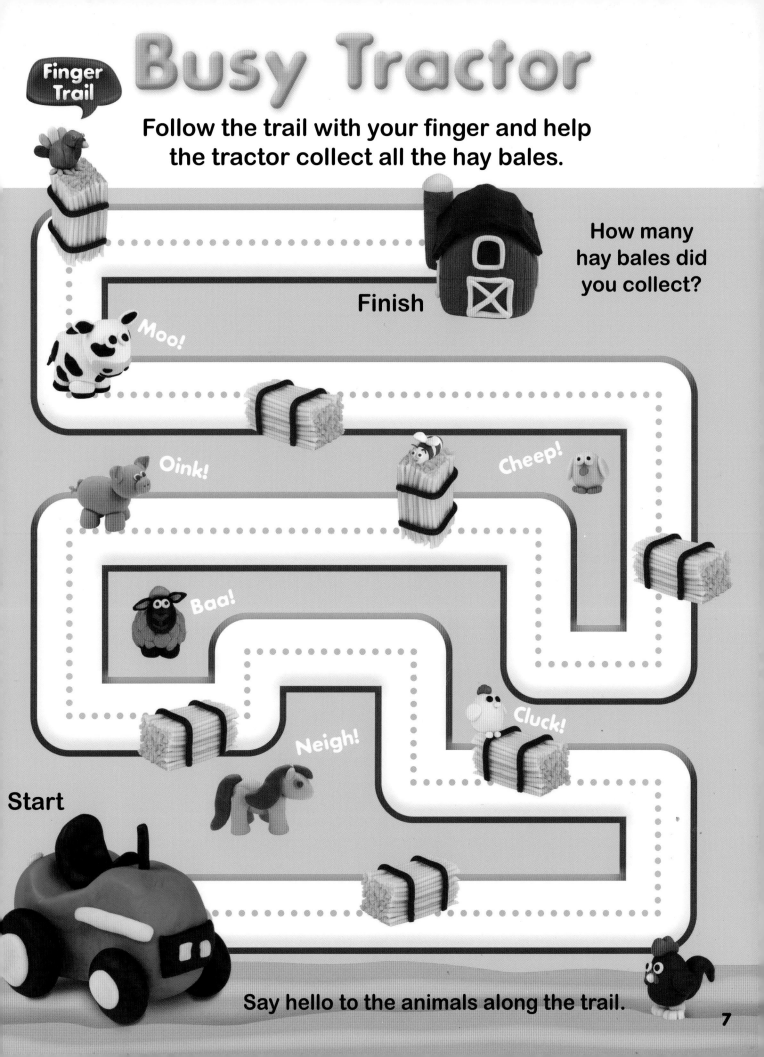

Busy Tractor

Finger Trail

Follow the trail with your finger and help the tractor collect all the hay bales.

How many hay bales did you collect?

Finish

Moo!

Oink!

Cheep!

Baa!

Neigh!

Cluck!

Start

Say hello to the animals along the trail.

Under the Sea

Ahoy there, shipmates! Are you ready to explore the Play-Doh seas? Can you find the ten sea creatures?

Can you spot the ten seashells?

Can you find the pearl?

Find two friends for the stripy fish!

Snap!

Where is the lobster's bucket?

Click! Click!

How many legs does the octopus have?

Glug! Glug!

8

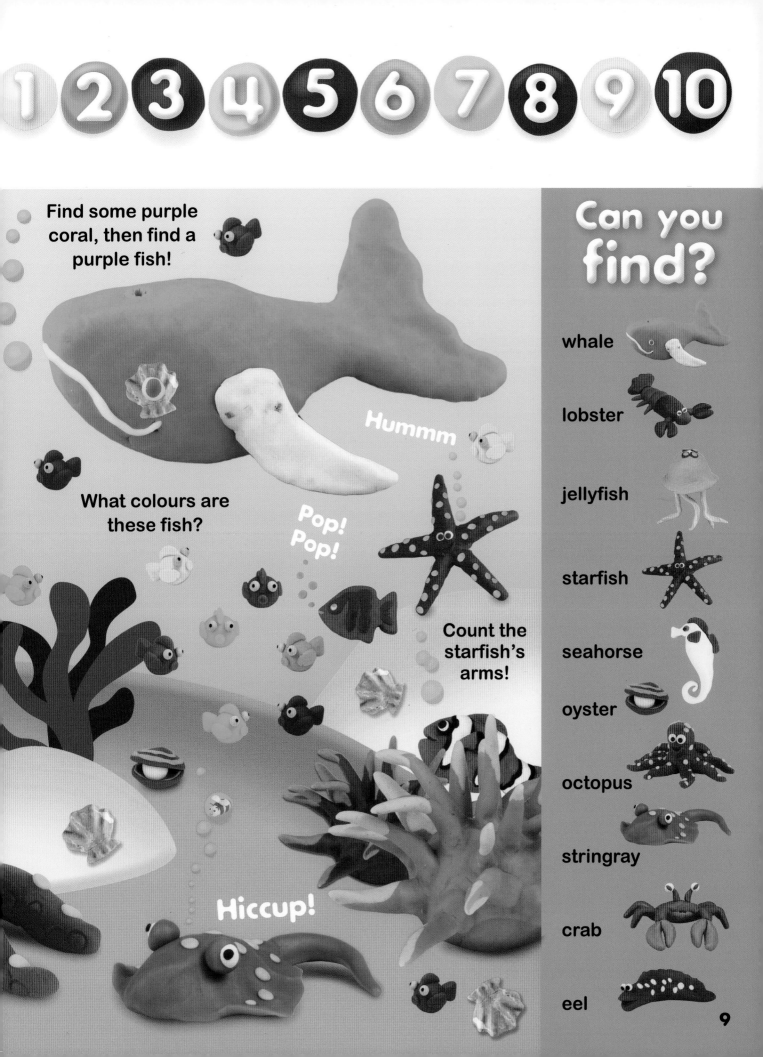

1 2 3 4 5 6 7 8 9 10

Find some purple coral, then find a purple fish!

Hummm

What colours are these fish?

Pop! Pop!

Count the starfish's arms!

Hiccup!

Can you find?

whale

lobster

jellyfish

starfish

seahorse

oyster

octopus

stringray

crab

eel

9

Big Fish, Little Fish

Can you find the biggest stripy fish and the smallest stripy fish?

How many
white stripes
do they have?

Which fish is the
odd one out?

If you made a Play-Doh fish, what colour would you make it?

Play-Doh

Sail Away

Follow the trail of pink boats from the start dot to the finish dot.
What fishy Play-Doh friends can you spot along the way?

Start

Finish

11

In the Jungle

Seek and Find

The Play-Doh jungle is green, hot, and full of noisy animals. Can you find and count the groups of jungle animal friends?

Can you find monkey's banana?

Can you count ten dragonflies?

Hoo! Hoo!

Which animal has a long neck?

Hi!

Hey!

Toot! Toot!

Find a friend for snake!

Hiss!

12

Wild Animal Pairs

Which wild creature doesn't have a pair?
Spot the animal that needs a friend.

Matching Pairs

What colour would you use to make a
friend for the animal without a pair?

Play-Doh

14

Animal Safari

Follow the trail with your finger and help the safari bus pass by all the animals.

Roar!

Finger Trail

● Start

Beep! Beep!

Say hello to the animals along the way.

Count the trees!

Hoo! Hoo!

Hiss!

Toot! Toot!

Can you make the animal sounds?

Squawk!

● Finish

Seek and Find

In the Garden

The Play-Doh garden is a happy place to be. Who is here today? Can you find and count all the garden creatures?

Can you spot the mouse who is hiding from the cat?

Woof!

Meow!

Flutter! Flutter!

Can you find the dog's ball?

How many toys can you see?

Scurry! Scurry!

Hop! Hop!

Can you find ten leaves?

Where has sleepy snail been?

16

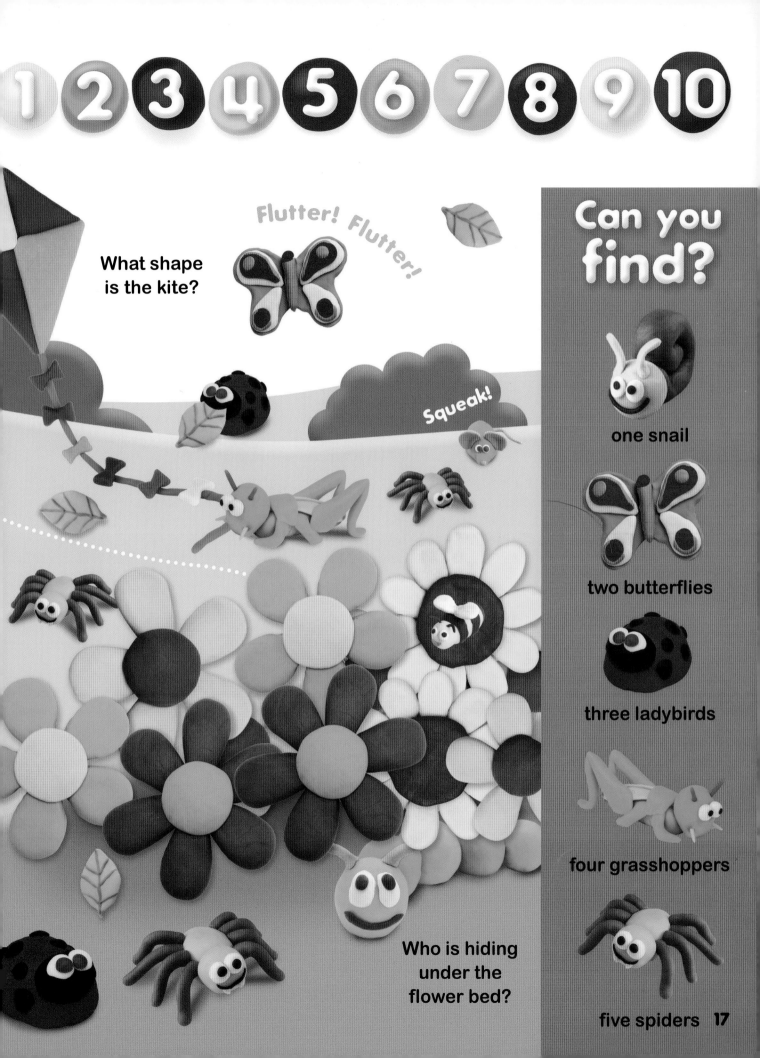

1 2 3 4 5 6 7 8 9 10

Flutter! Flutter!

What shape is the kite?

Squeak!

Who is hiding under the flower bed?

Can you find?

one snail

two butterflies

three ladybirds

four grasshoppers

five spiders **17**

Count Ten

Can you find ten carrots in the vegetable patch for the bouncing bunnies to eat?

What other vegetables can you name?

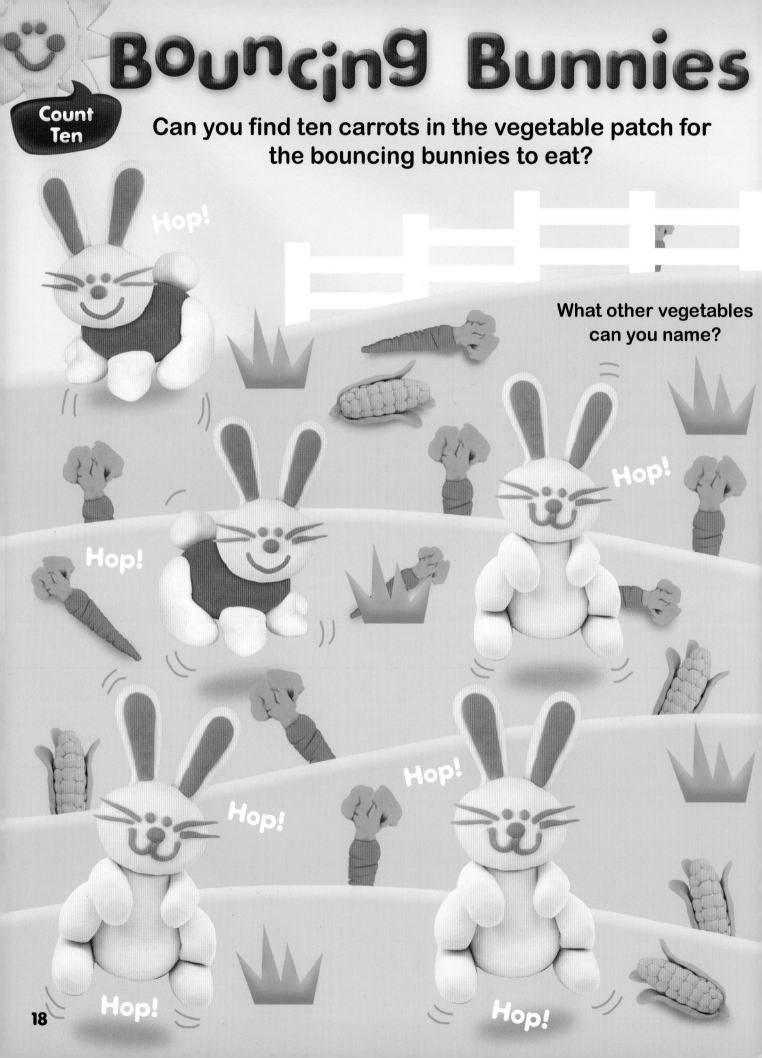

Petal Counting

Count the petals on each pretty flower below.
Which flower has the most petals?

Now can you work out which flower has the fewest petals?

Which creatures love the flowers?

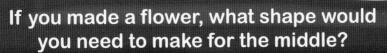

If you made a flower, what shape would you need to make for the middle?

Play-Doh

19

In the Town

The town is full of Play-Doh things that go, both on the ground and in the sky. Can you find and count all the town things in the picture?

Chug! Chug!

Ding!

Nee! Naw!

Find the ladder to rescue the cat.

What can you spot in the sky today?

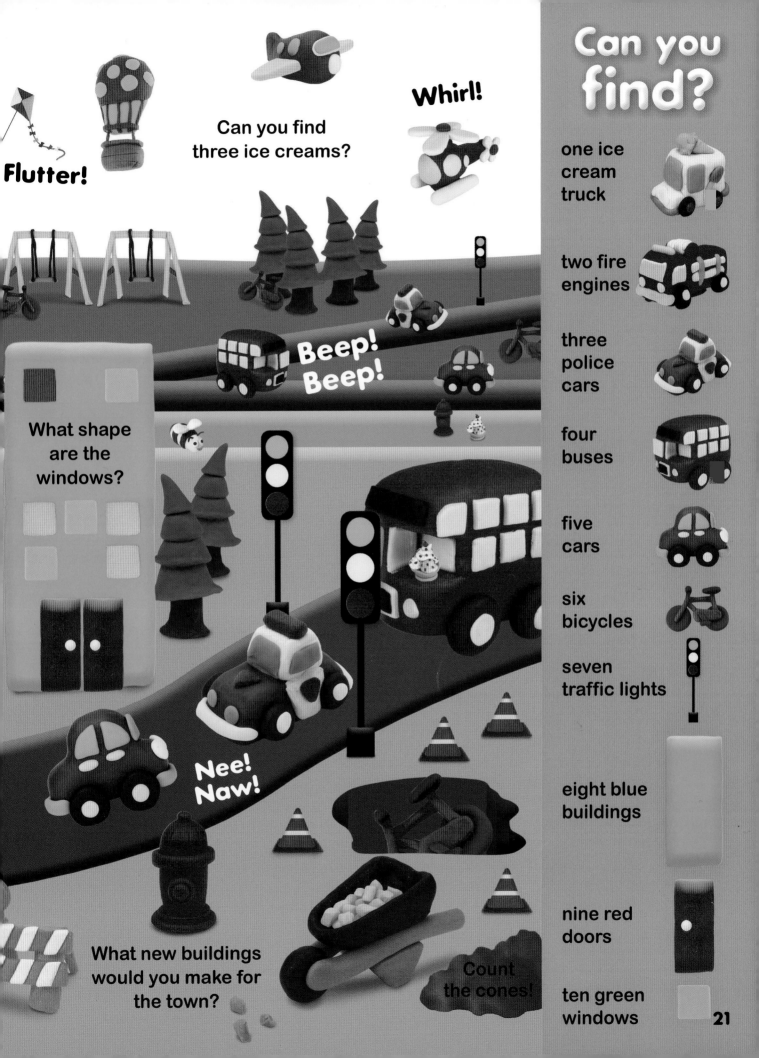

Flutter!

Whirl!

Can you find
three ice creams?

Beep!
Beep!

What shape
are the
windows?

Nee!
Naw!

What new buildings
would you make for
the town?

Count
the cones!

Can you find?

one ice cream truck

two fire engines

three police cars

four buses

five cars

six bicycles

seven traffic lights

eight blue buildings

nine red doors

ten green windows

21

Answers

Page 4 and 5

Page 6 and 7

Page 8 and 9

Answers

Page 10 and 11

Page 12 and 13

Page 14 and 15

Answers

Page 16 and 17

Page 18 and 19

Page 20 and 21

24